A band called Take That

A band called Take That

A Popjustice Book
Illustrated by David Whittle

First published in Great Britain in 2006 by Friday Books
An imprint of The Friday Project Limited
83 Victoria Street, London SW1H 0HW

www.thefridayproject.co.uk
www.fridaybooks.co.uk

Text © Peter Robinson 2006
Illustrations © David Whittle 2006

ISBN – 10   1 905548 24 9
ISBN – 13   978 1 905548 24 8

British Library Cataloguing in Publication Data

A catalogue record for this book is available
from the British Library

Designed and produced by Staziker Jones
www.stazikerjones.co.uk

The Publisher's policy is to use paper
manufactured from sustainable sources

This book belongs to

_____

I am ____ years old

My favourite Take That song is _____

When I grow up, I want to be _____

Here is my autograph!

_____

Once upon a time there was a man called Nigel.

Nigel liked pop songs and he liked boys singing pop songs. He particularly liked a group of boys from America. They were called New Kids On The Block.

New Kids On The Block were very popular all around the world.

A light bulb appeared above Nigel's head. What if there was a British version of New Kids On The Block?

It would be very good!

But where would Nigel find British boys?

There was a knock on the door.

In walked two boys. One of them was called Howard, the other was called Jason.

Jason liked to dance around and so did Howard.

Nigel liked Howard and Jason, but Nigel needed more boys to make the new New Kids On The Block.

There was another knock on the door!

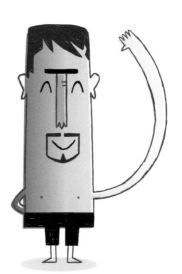

In walked another two boys! One of them was called Gary, the other was called Mark.

Gary liked to write songs and Mark was very good at dancing around. Gary was not very keen on dancing around. He wasn't very good at it.

It was time to find another member for the band.

There was a knock at the door.

Unfortunately it was just the cleaner.

Nigel and the boys set up an audition to find the band's fifth member.

In walked a boy called Robbie.

'I'm Robbie,' said Robbie.

'You're in the band!' said Nigel and the boys.

Take That were ready to conquer the world!

Take That performed some pop concerts in small places like schools.

To begin with nobody was very interested in this new band.

But one day they performed in some special nightclubs for men who love each other.

Nigel knew that men who love each other like to look at other men with all their clothes off.

Suddenly, all Take That's clothes fell off!

Unfortunately, every time Take That released a song, nobody bought it!

The band were very upset about this. They did not realise that it was because their songs were a bit rubbish!

They had one last try with a song called 'It Only Takes A Minute'. It was good and it was a song about things that did not take very long.

Take That became huge stars!

They were on all the TV programmes and in all the magazines.

Because of this they had some more hit records!

SMASH HITS
HOW To SCrEAM!
Latest Tapes Reviewed
Full FTSE 100 INDEX!
TAKE THAT!
The Bestest Band Ever!

In 1994 Gary received an award for writing good songs. He became 'Songwriter Of The Year', which meant that for twelve months he had been better than everyone else at writing songs.

This cheered Gary up because it proved that you did not have to be a good dancer in order to be popular.

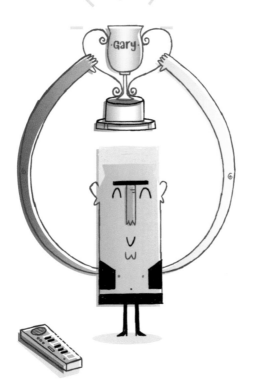

Later in the year everyone in the band got their hair cut.

This was to prove that they were old enough to go into a hairdresser's shop by themselves.

Take That had grown up!

Take That were so famous that when
Princess Diana organised a concert,
she invited Take That to perform.

Unfortunately a few years later Diana was
horribly killed in a massive car accident.

But this was not Take That's fault.

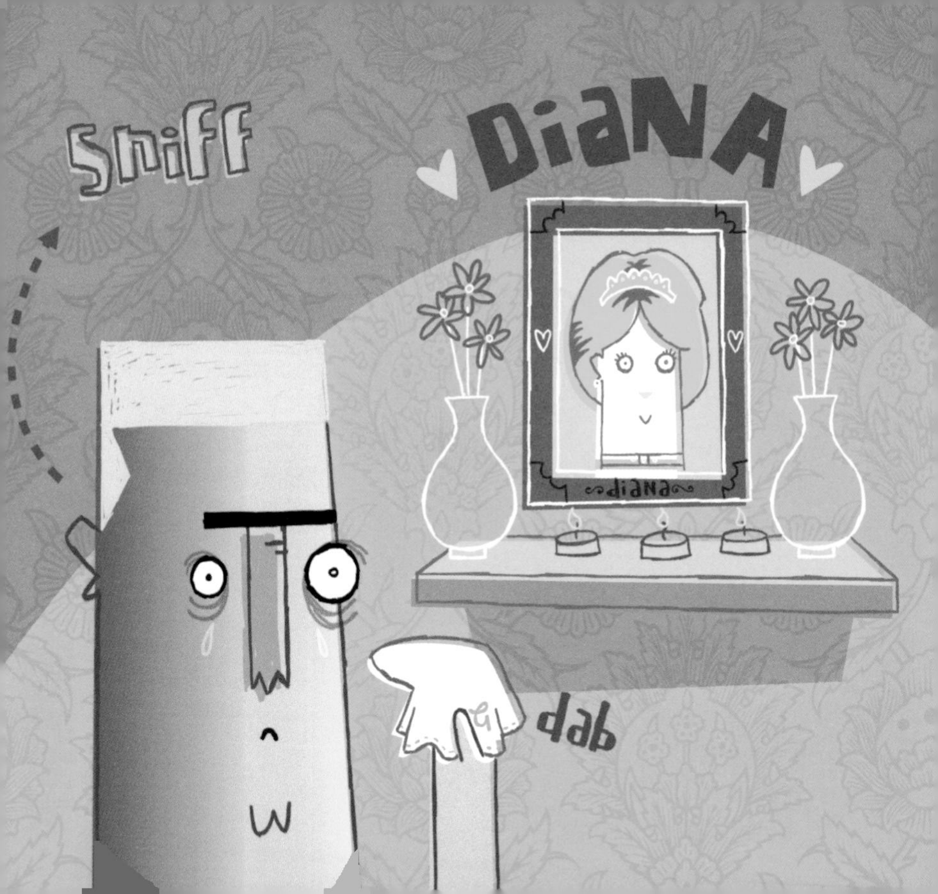

Sniff
DiaNA
diaNa
dab

In 1995, Take That sang a song at a very famous awards ceremony called The Brits.

It was a new song called 'Back For Good', and nobody had heard it before.

Suddenly, even old people realised that Take That were brilliant!

One day Robbie decided that he was bored of being in Take That.

Robbie left the band and it was a very sad day.

There were lots of rumours that without Robbie the band would split up.

Unfortunately, the rumours were true.

In 1996, the day before Valentine's Day, Take That held a press conference to say that they were not going to be together any more.

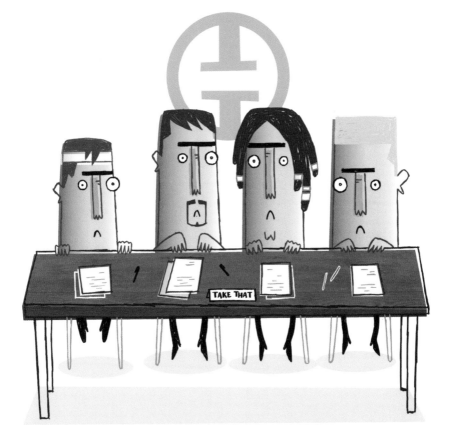

Take That's fans weren't very happy with this news.

After the band split up, Gary, Jason, Howard and Mark didn't really know what to do.

Jason became an actor. Howard worked in discos putting songs on one after another. Mark kept on being a popstar.

Gary tried to be a popstar but then decided to sit at home writing songs for other popstars.

By 2005, the boys realised that they missed each other.

Because they enjoyed press conferences so much, they held another one.

This time it was good news – Take That were getting back together! Everyone wept with joy at this amazing news.

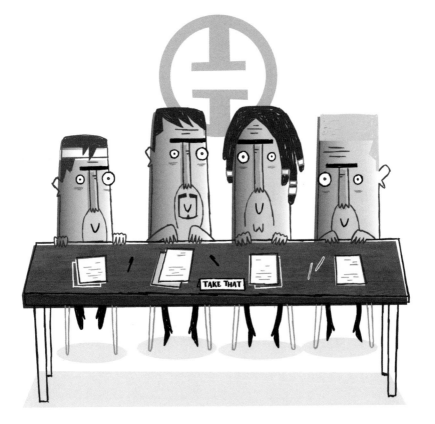

It was not long before Take That were on another big tour.

Because everyone was now quite old, they didn't dance around very much.

Can you guess who liked this idea?

That's right – our old friend Gary!

The End

Here are Robbie and his friend Nigel Martin Smith. Robbie is one fifth of Take That and Nigel has one fifth of Robbie's piggy bank.

Cut out Robbie and Nigel (be careful with the sharp edges!) and act out special scenes with them.

Robbie: I'm famous and bored.
Nigel: Bye then!
Robbie: Oh.

Have fun!

Popjustice.com is the greatest pop website on the face of Planet Earth. We update every day with the best pop stuff.

Drop in at **www.popjustice.com/idols** for downloadable wallpapers, screensavers and other random nonsense.

Why not send us an email? idols@popjustice.com